My Puppy

by Anne Brailsford
photographs by Wolf Kutnahorsky

Scholastic Canada Ltd.

My puppy needs food.

My puppy needs water.

My puppy needs a collar.

My puppy needs a leash.

My puppy needs a toy.

My puppy needs me!

What My Puppy Needs

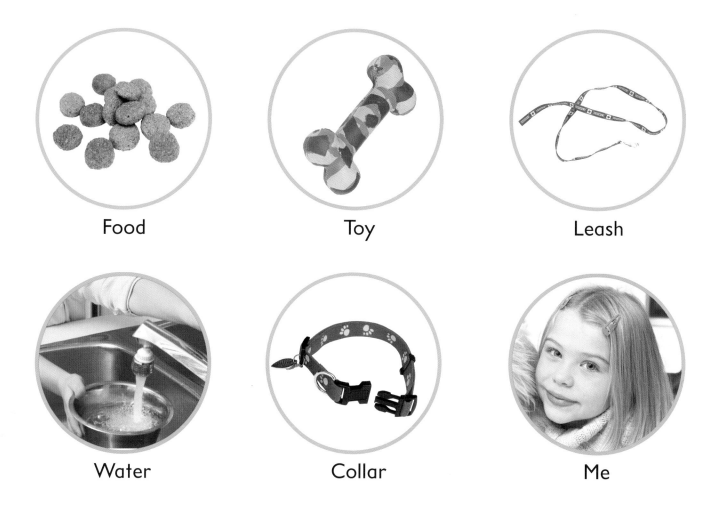

Food

Toy

Leash

Water

Collar

Me